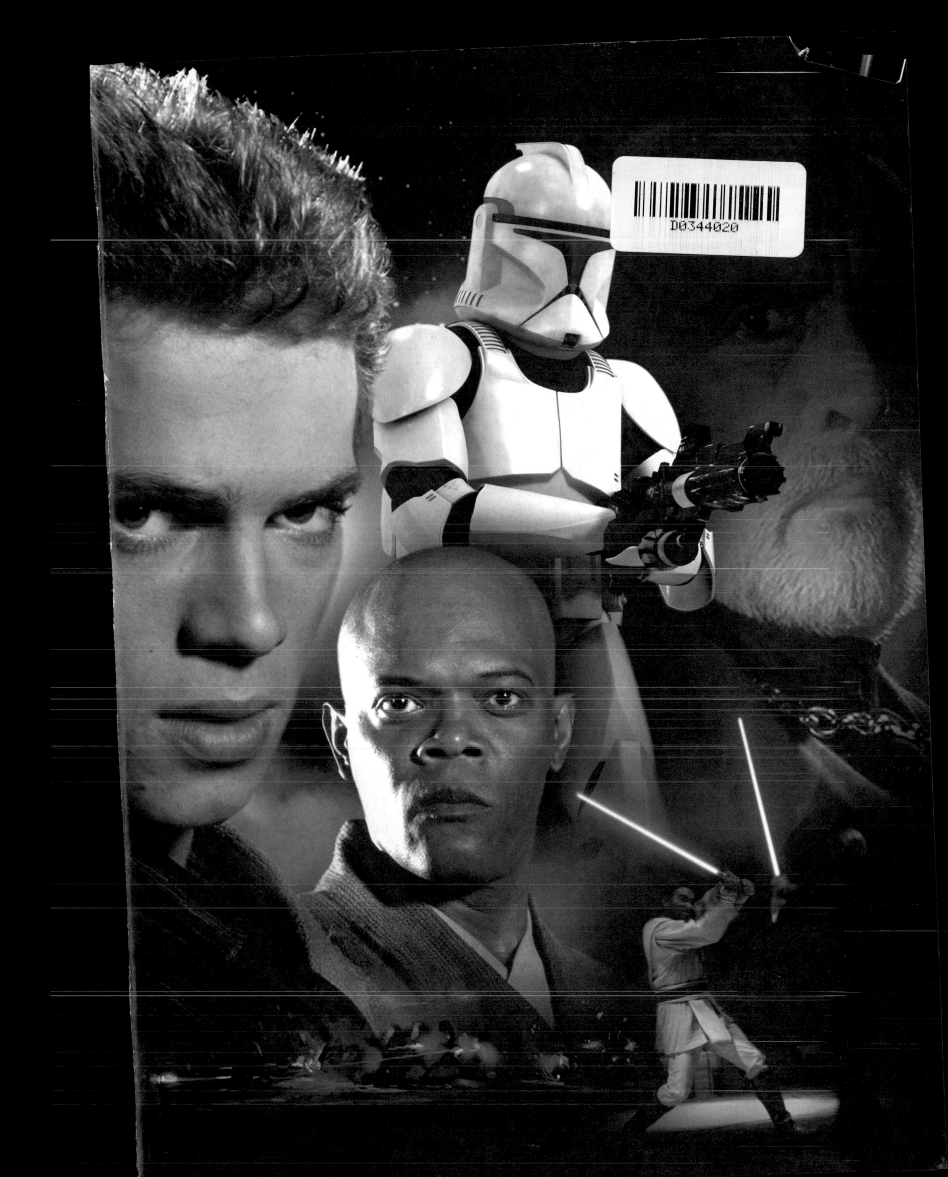

# CONTENTS

# STAR WARS ™

Published by Pedigree Books Limited
Beech Hill House, Walnut Gardens, Exeter, Devon EX4 4DH.
E-mail books@pedigreegroup.co.uk
Published 2004

£7.99

PADAWAN PROBLEMS?

HE DOESN'T ALWAYS LISTEN. HE RARELY EVER TALKS. HE'S IMPATIENT. HE'S RESTLESS. HE'S MOODY. HE'S ARROGANT. HE'S... DIFFICULT, QUINLAN.

SINCE GEONOSIS, IT'S AS IF A CHASM HAS OPENED BETWEEN US. THERE HAS BEEN NO TIME TO STOP... SORT THINGS THROUGH...

YOU FEEL AS IF YOU'RE FAILING HIM?

IN A WAY. YES.

BEFORE HE DIED, MY MASTER, QUI-GON JINN, ENTRUSTED ME WITH ANAKIN. TO MAKE SURE THAT HE BECAME A KNIGHT. I GAVE MY OATH. I... NEVER REALLY CHOSE ANAKIN AS MY PADAWAN.

MAYBE IT'S TIME YOU DID.

THEN THE QUESTION IS -- DO I TRUST HIM? DO I TRUST MYSELF?

JANGO
FETT

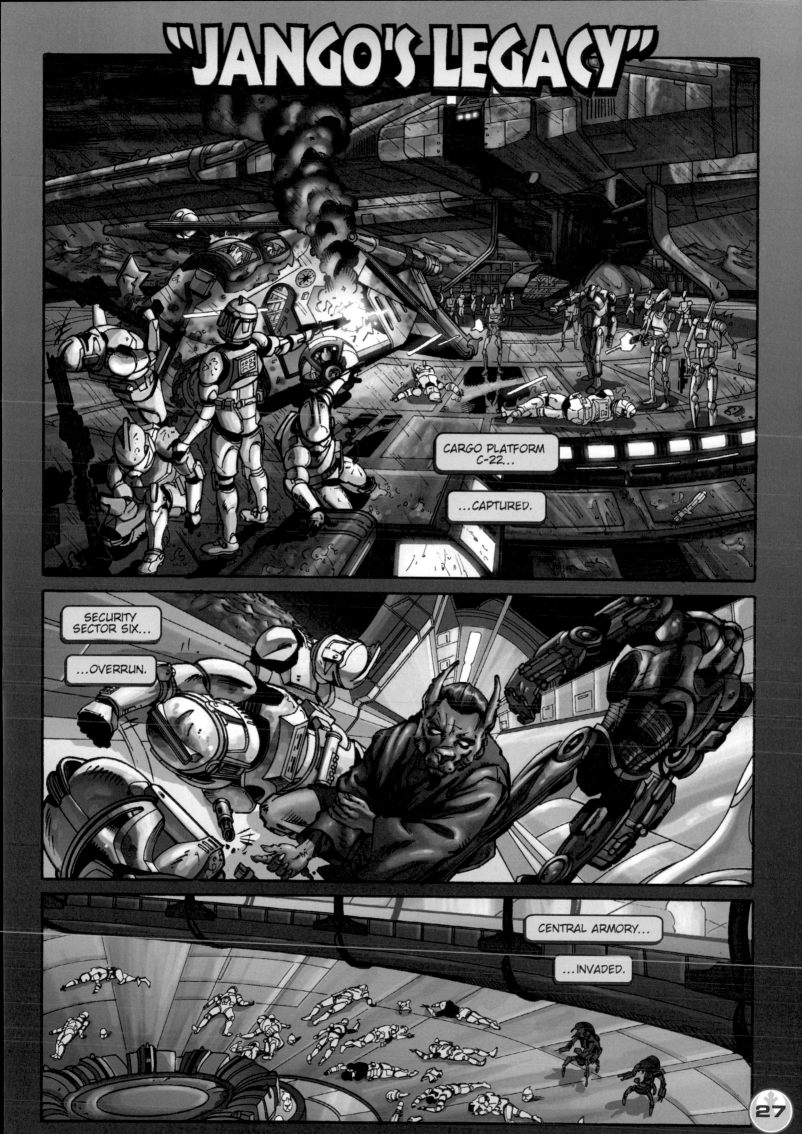

41

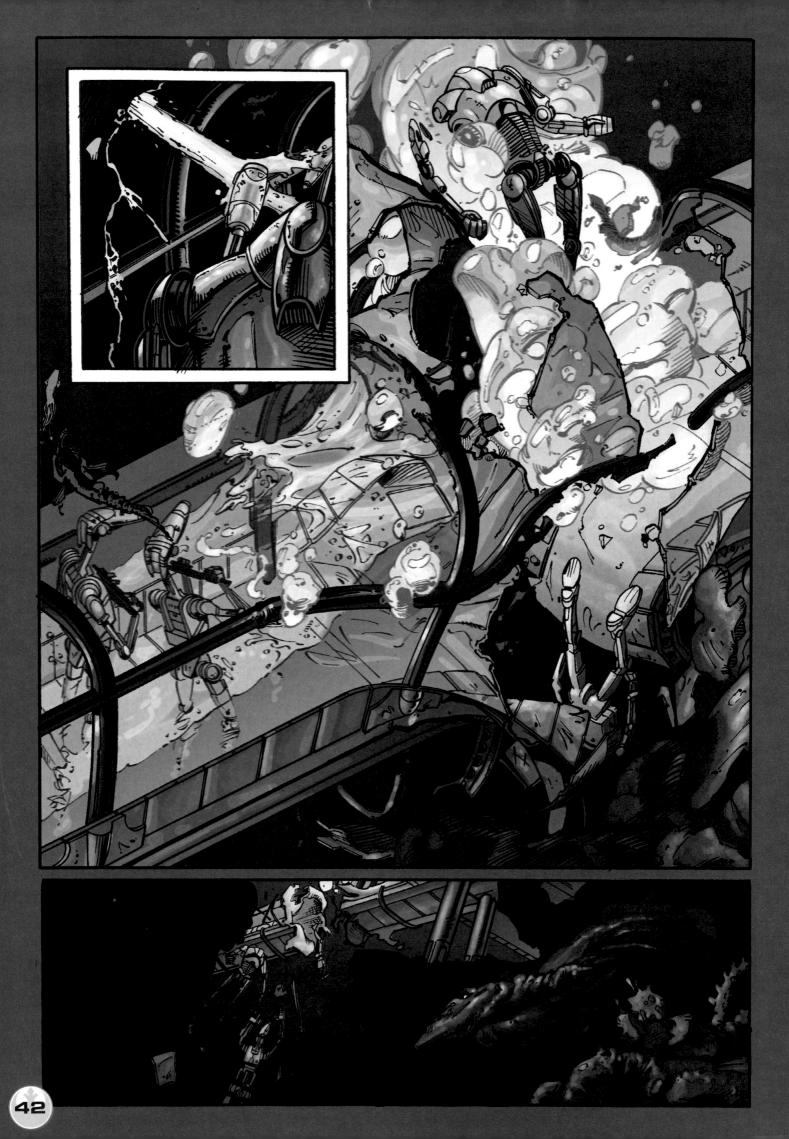

STAR WARS™

45

"NO END IN SIGHT"

"-- I WANT THEM *DIRECTLY* OVER THE CLONING FACILITY WHEN THAT SHIELD GOES DOWN."

COMMANDER MERAI, WE'RE *LOSING* THIS ONE!

WE MUST *RETREAT!* WE HAVEN'T GOT A LIMITLESS SUPPLY OF DROIDS -- OR MEN!

*WE'VE MORE DROIDS* THAN THEY HAVE *JEDI.* TWO OF THEIR *ACES* JUST HIT THE WATER AT ONCE!

I WANT *FIVE* OF OUR AMPHIBIOUS FIGHTERS TO SUBMERGE. *FLANK THEM* WITH *TEN* DROID FIGHTERS ON EITHER SIDE.

AND START HITTING THOSE *JEDI STARFIGHTERS* HARDER -- MAKE THEM THINK *THEY'RE* OUR FOCUS.

-- BUT WE'VE GOT COMPANY --

AHHHHHH -- ⸾BZZT⸿

EVERY ONE OF THEM ... THE JEDI MUST'VE *SENSED* WHAT THEY WERE DOING...

FEED THOSE COORDINATES TO *THE SHARK.*

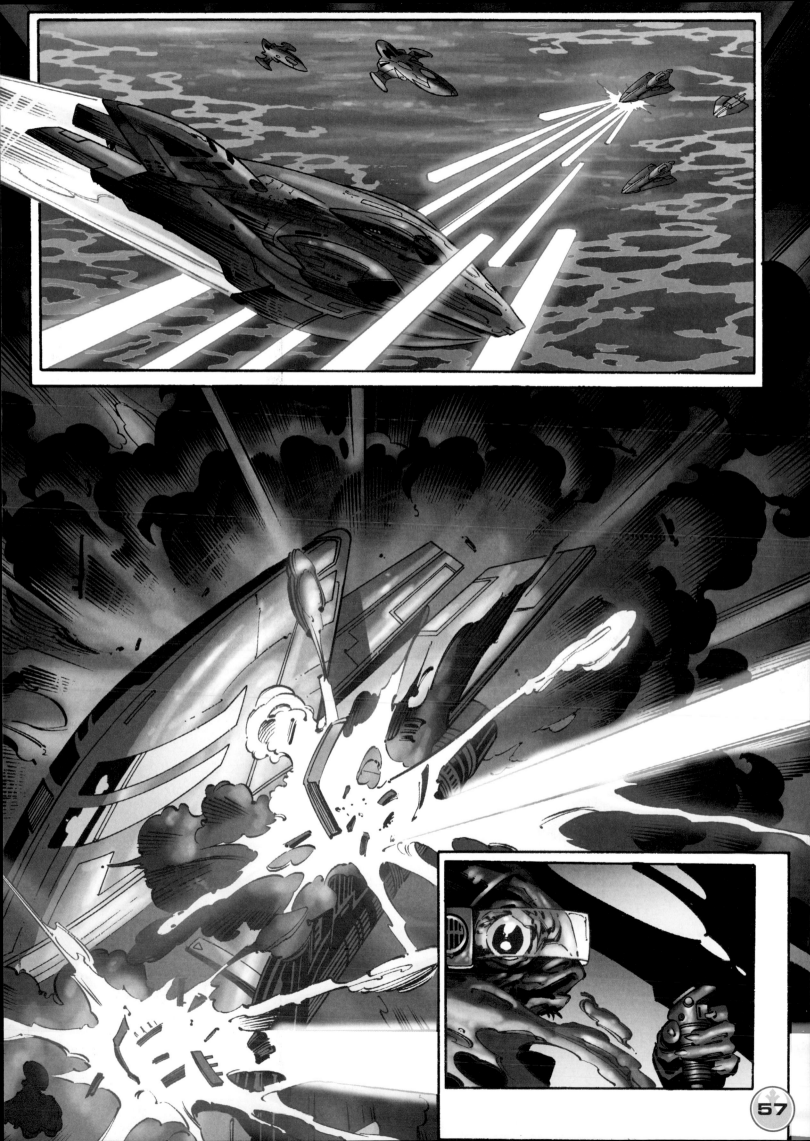

THE COMMANDER'S SHIP IS DAMAGED!

DON'T COUNT HIM OUT, YET...

MEN. I WANT YOU TO RETREAT.

YOU NEED TO HELP ME SEND THE SHARK *STRAIGHT* UP -- I'LL *STEER*, YOU JUST *BOOST* MY JETS WITH THE CORE SHIP'S *TRACTOR BEAMS.*

Y-YES, SIR, BUT WE WON'T BE ABLE TO COORDINATE THE *DROID ATTACKS* --

THE DROIDS NEED TO BE *WITHDRAWN.*

THEY'RE NEEDED ELSEWHERE. THE AMPHIBIOUS SQUADS, TOO -- FOR BATTLES WHERE YOU STAND A CHANCE.

BUT SIR. IF-IF WE DO THAT, *HALF* THE SHIPS MAY BE PICKED OFF BY THE REPUBLIC FORCES -- THE JEDI MIGHT EVEN FOLLOW US BACK TO THE BASE.

EVADE THEIR SHOTS AS BEST YOU CAN. I'LL MAKE SURE THE JEDI DON'T FOLLOW YOU. NOW GIVE ME THAT BOOST...

THE LAST SHIPS ARE DOCKING!

PREPARE FOR HYPERSPACE!

COMMANDER MERAI -- YOU'VE ENGAGED YOUR SHIP'S *SELF-DESTRUCT* --

NEVER MIND THAT -- *MAKE THE JUMP!* GET TO SAFETY!

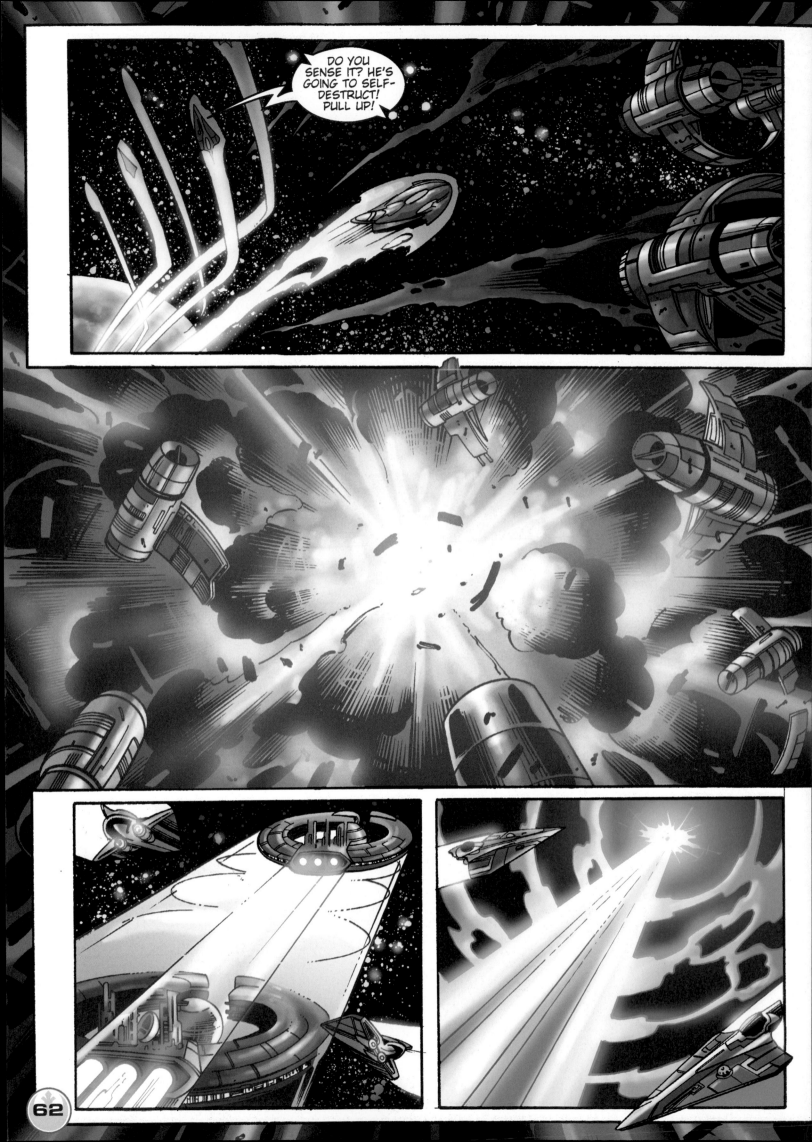

ADI GALLIA WAS TOO HARD ON HERSELF. SHE FELT SHE SHOULD HAVE EXPECTED THE SABOTAGE OF THE HYPERSPACE RINGS. I TOLD HER TO TAKE SOLACE IN OUR VICTORY. KAMINO'S SAFE, AND I DOUBT THE FEDERATION WILL TRY ANOTHER ATTACK.

YET YOU AS WELL SEEM UNSATISFIED, MY FRIEND.

IT'S THE MON CALAMARI LEADER. MERAI. I KNEW HIM. KNEW OF HIM.

HE WAS A SMART SOLDIER. WHY WOULD HE ATTEMPT SUCH AN ILL-PLANNED ATTACK? AND ON WHOSE ORDERS?

DARKER AND MORE CLOUDED THE FUTURE IS...

THE END

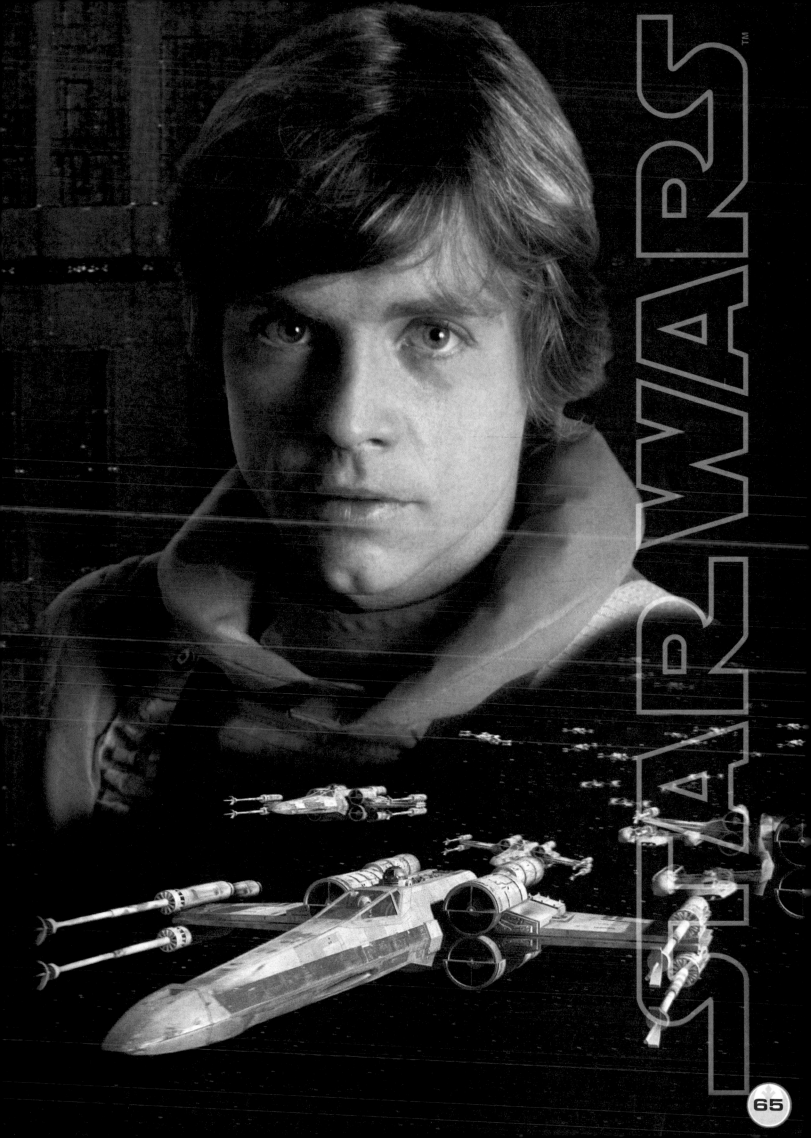

STAR WARS™

"ENERGY BECOMES MATTER; MATTER BECOMES ENERGY." THIS IS TRUTH.

"THERE IS NO DEATH; THERE IS ONLY THE FORCE." WE ALSO HOLD THIS TO BE TRUE. WE RELEASE MASTER VOOKTO'S MATTER TO AGAIN BECOME ENERGY, ONE WITH THE FORCE.

THIS DOES NOT MEAN WE DO NOT FEEL SORROW AT HIS PASSING.

TRUE TO HIS DUROS HERITAGE, MASTER VOOKTO LOVED TO TRAVEL AND OFTEN WENT ON LONG JOURNEY MISSIONS AT THE OUTER EDGES OF THE REPUBLIC.

HE TRAINED TWO PADAWANS, THE MOST RECENT BEING *DAMA MONTALVO* HERE.

MISS, WILL I, STORIES HE WOULD TELL OF HIS TRAVELS. QUIET HIS VOICE WAS, DRY HIS HUMOR.

HE SACRIFICED HIS OWN LIFE TODAY FOR HIS TROOPS, WHO WOULD HAVE SACRIFICED THEIR OWN FOR HIS.

"THIS WAS HIS VICTORY."

WHEN THE CALL CAME, MASTER VOOKTO RETURNED IMMEDIATELY AND TOOK COMMAND OF AN ARMY, WITHOUT HESITATION OR QUESTION, AND LED ABLY.

DAMA, MASTER KI-ADI-MUNDI IS HERE TO TAKE CHARGE OF MASTER VOOKTO'S TROOPS. FOR THE PRESENT, GO WITH HIM. WE WILL SPEAK AGAIN LATER.

PART OF A LARGER PROBLEM. MASTERS *THOLME* AND *VOS*, GIVE ME YOUR REPORT, PLEASE.

MANY MASTERLESS PADAWANS HAVE WE NOW. MORE WE WILL. DEAL WITH IT, WE MUST.

IN THE THREE MONTHS SINCE THIS WAR BEGAN, WE'VE LOST A GREAT MANY JEDI. OUR FORCES ARE SCRAPED THIN AS IT IS. THE PROBLEM HAS BEEN MADE WORSE BY THE NUMBER OF JEDI WHO HAVE *REFUSED* TO SERVE AS GENERALS.

AS YOU REQUESTED, QUINLAN MADE CONTACT WITH FOUR OF THE LEADERS OF THE DISSIDENT JEDI -- JEISEL, K'KRUHK, RHAD TARN, AND MIRA.

THEY'VE BEEN JOINED AND UNITED NOW BY MASTER *SORA BULQ.*

SORA BULQ! THAT *IS* NEWS.

JEISEL WAS ALWAYS PLAIN ABOUT HER REFUSAL TO BE A GENERAL, AND K'KRUHK WAS THOUGHT DEAD. BUT SORA WAS A *TEACHER* AT THE TEMPLE -- LIGHTSABER INSTRUCTION...

WHEN I DEVELOPED *VAAPAD,* SORA WAS THE ONE I PRACTICED WITH. HE'S ONE OF THE FEW WHO KNOWS IT ALMOST AS WELL AS I DO.

HE RE-EDUCATED *ME* AFTER MY MEMORY LOSS.

YOU'VE RECOVERED YOUR MEMORY -- BUT WHAT ABOUT YOUR SKILLS?

I UNDERSTAND YOU'VE BEEN CARRYING A *BLASTER* WHILE UNDER-COVER?

MASTER BULQ.

MASTER WINDU. WELCOME.

I APOLOGIZE FOR THE POOR HOSPITALITY OF MY FAMILY'S ESTATE.

BEING A JEDI, I HAD NO USE FOR IT BEFORE NOW. I HAVE SET DROIDS TO CLEARING AND REPAIRING A PORTION OF IT.

COMFORT IS NOT MY CONCERN. THIS POTENTIAL SCHISM CONCERNS ME MORE -- AS DO YOU. WHY DID YOU NOT COME TO ME AND TALK?

YOU VANISHED AFTER GEONOSIS, AND THE NEXT I HEAR YOU'VE JOINED THESE DISSIDENTS. WHY?

I COULDN'T TALK. MY HEART WAS TOO FULL. ALMOST EVERY JEDI WHO DIED ON GEONOSIS I HAD TRAINED AT SOME POINT.

I SPARRED WITH QUINLAN VOS RECENTLY. HE USED A MOVE FROM VAAPAD -- A MOVE HE SAID YOU TAUGHT HIM.

I WAS TESTING HIM. HE PASSED THE TEST SO I WENT NO FURTHER. WHY?

THEY DIED TO PRESERVE THE REPUBLIC, AND I AM NOT SURE THE REPUBLIC IS WORTH THAT. UNTIL I AM SURE, I THOUGHT IT BEST TO ABSENT MYSELF.

NOTHING. WHICH WAY DO YOU INTEND TO SIDE IN THESE DISCUSSIONS? YOU HAVE A TREMENDOUS INFLUENCE.

I HAVE NO IDEA. I WILL LISTEN, MEDITATE, AND THEN PERHAPS I WILL DECIDE.

WAIT HERE, MASTER WINDU. I WILL BRING THE OTHERS TO YOU AND WE CAN BEGIN.

MASTER K'KRUHK.

MASTER WINDU. GREETINGS.

WE HAD THOUGHT YOU SLAIN WITH YOUR TROOPS ON TEYR.

I'M GLAD TO HEAR YOU LIVE -- BUT SADDENED THAT YOU NO LONGER WALK WITH US.

WHY?

YOU *KNOW* ME, MASTER WINDU. YOU WERE THERE WHEN MY FIRST MASTER ... LILIT TWOSEAS ... WAS KILLED. THE FOURTH PRECEPT ... "NO DEATH, ONLY THE FORCE," IS HARD FOR ME.

WHEN THE CALL CAME AFTER GEONOSIS, I OBEYED. I TOOK COMMAND OF A BATTALION OF CLONE TROOPERS ON TEYR. I LED THEM INTO BATTLE. I LEAD FROM THE FRONT, NOT FROM BEHIND. I KNOW NO OTHER WAY. THE BATTLE ... DID NOT GO WELL FOR US THAT DAY.

FALL BACK!

WE CAN ACHIEVE THE OBJECTIVE, GENERAL. WE NEED TO PRESS ON.

MOST OF YOU WILL DIE IN THE PROCESS. THAT IS NOT ACCEPTABLE TO ME.

WITH RESPECT, SIR -- IT IS WHAT WE WERE BRED FOR. TO BATTLE, TO OBEY, AND TO DIE, IF NEED BE. THAT'S ALL.

AS A JEDI, I WAS TAUGHT TO PRESERVE LIFE. I LED THESE CLONES -- NO, THESE *MEN* -- TO THEIR DEATHS.

THESE WERE LIVING, SENTIENT BEINGS. WHAT I HAVE BEEN ASKED TO DO IS THE OPPOSITE OF EVERYTHING I WAS TRAINED TO DO AS A JEDI. IT BETRAYS EVERYTHING I BELIEVE WE ARE MEANT TO *BE* AS JEDI. HOW CAN YOU ASK THIS?

80

WHEN I WAS A PADAWAN, WE SPENT ALMOST ALL OF OUR TIME OUT IN THE FRINGES OF THE REPUBLIC ON JOURNEY MISSIONS. I'VE *SEEN* THE RESULTS OF THE REPUBLIC'S CORRUPTION!

DO YOU THINK THE COUNCIL HAS NOT CONSIDERED YOUR QUESTIONS -- *ALL* OF YOUR QUESTIONS -- BEFORE? THAT WE DO NOT *STILL*? DO YOU THINK YOUR WISDOM *GREATER* THAN, SAY, MASTER YODA'S?

THE SENATE DOESN'T *CARE* ABOUT SLAVE TRADE, OR ILLEGAL PRISONS, OR THE LABORERS IN THE SPICE MINES! NOT SO LONG AS THE *POCKETS* OF SENATORS *BULGE*!

AND WE JEDI *ARE* TAINTED BY OUR CONNECTIONS TO THE REPUBLIC! MANY SEE US AT ITS *ENFORCERS*! WE'RE ON THE *WRONG SIDE*! WE SHOULD BE HELPING TO BRING THE REPUBLIC *DOWN* -- ONCE AND FOR ALL!

MASTER BULQ, WHAT DO *YOU* THINK?

FOR MYSELF, I DO NOT FEEL I CAN SUPPORT THE REPUBLIC. MORE THAN THAT -- I DO NOT YET KNOW.

I WAS RELUCTANT TO SAY ANYTHING BUT... THERE *IS* WISDOM OUTSIDE OF CORUSCANT. I WORRY THAT THE COUNCIL SEES WHAT IT *WANTS* TO SEE AND WILL ACT AS IT HAS *ALWAYS* ACTED.

IT GROWS LATE. I SUGGEST WE SEPARATE FOR TONIGHT. THINK, MEDITATE, REST, SLEEP. TALK AGAIN IN THE MORNING.

COME, MASTER WINDU. LET ME SHOW YOU THE WAY TO THE MAIN HOUSE.

RHAD, BE CAREFUL OF WHAT YOU SAY...

NO, MASTER BULQ, I WILL *NOT*!

*NO* SHIP CAN LAND ON YOUR ESTATE, MASTER BULQ, WITHOUT YOU'RE KNOWING IT, RIGHT? THIS KILLER DIDN'T COME WITH ANY OF *US*! THE LAST SHIP TO LAND WAS MASTER WINDU'S! THE KILLER *HAD* TO HAVE COME WITH HIM!

EXCEPT THAT SHE DID NOT.

REMAIN HERE AND TEND TO MASTER BULQ. I WILL FIND -- AND DEAL WITH -- THIS ASSASSIN.

HE'S LYING! SHE'S *HIS* ASSASSIN...!

NO. THAT IS NOT HIS WAY. IF MASTER WINDU DESIRED US DEAD, HE WOULDN'T NEED AN ASSASSIN. ONLY MASTER BULQ MIGHT BE ABLE TO WITHSTAND HIM.

IT IS SIMPLY NOT THE MACE WINDU I KNOW.

*DO* YOU KNOW HIM, K'KRUHK? DO *ANY* OF US *REALLY* KNOW MASTER WINDU?

FOLLOW HIM.

I THINK THEY'RE IN THIS TOGETHER! I'M GOING TO FIND THEM AND *PROVE* IT!

I DON'T WISH TO LEAVE YOU ALONE, MASTER BULQ. YOU WERE HURT IN THE BATTLE AND MASTER WINDU SAID TO REMAIN...

HE SAID TO STICK TOGETHER -- THE *THREE* OF YOU. MY WOUND IS NOT SERIOUS -- NOR IMPORTANT.

I WILL TAKE MIRA BACK TO THE HOUSE. I WILL BE ALL RIGHT. GO. FIND YOUR BROTHER JEDI.

"FIND MACE WINDU."

DON'T LET RHAD FACE THIS ASSASSIN -- OR MASTER WINDU -- ALONE.

I WAS LONG FASCINATED BY IT. OUR WORK ON VAAPAD -- MY OWN SECRET RESEARCHES INTO IT -- FASCINATED ME MORE.

WHAT I SAID ABOUT GEONOSIS WAS TRUE -- SAVE ONLY THAT COUNT DOOKU APPROACHED ME AFTER THE BATTLE WAS OVER.

THE DECIMATION OF THE JEDI ON GEONOSIS *DISGUSTED* ME. DOOKU SHOWED ME THAT IF THERE IS EVER TO BE A CHANGE IN THE REPUBLIC, WE *JEDI* MUST MAKE THAT CHANGE.

KKKKK

ONLY THE JEDI HOLD TRUE TO THE *PRINCIPLES* OF THE REPUBLIC, SO WE JEDI MUST BE PREPARED TO *RULE* -- SOMETHING THE COUNCIL WOULD *NEVER* ALLOW.

THE *PLAN* WAS TO *LURE* YOU AND THE OTHERS HERE, KILL ONE OR TWO, AND THEN BLAME *YOU* FOR THEIR DEATHS. THE SCHISM WOULD WIDEN, AND MANY MORE JEDI WOULD JOIN *US*.

NOW, I THINK IT'S BEST YOU *ALL* DIE AND I *ALONE* SURVIVE TO TELL THE TALE OF YOUR BETRAYAL. I WILL BE BELIEVED BECAUSE OF WHO I AM. AND COUNT DOOKU AND I WILL *FORGE* OUR FOLLOWERS INTO A WEAPON TO REMAKE THE GALAXY!

A SMALL *FLAW* IN YOUR PLAN --

-- I AM NOT DEAD.

LIVE TO FIGHT ANOTHER DAY.

WE ... CANNOT LET HER ... GET AWAY ... MASTER WINDU...

WHAT IF SHE GOES AFTER MASTER BULQ?!

SORA BULQ IS IN LEAGUE WITH THE ASSASSIN. THEIR EARLIER FIGHT WAS A SHAM MEANT TO DECEIVE.

OKAY, I'M CONVINCED.

TO MY SHIP. FOLLOW MY LEAD.

ARE YOU TAKING US BACK TO THE TEMPLE, MASTER WINDU?

ACTUALLY, I'D PREFER YOU GO TO THOSE YOU REPRESENT -- AND THAT RHAD AND MIRA REPRESENTED. LET THEM KNOW THE *TRUTH*. WARN THEM ABOUT SORA BULQ.

WHAT YOU DO AFTER THAT IS YOUR CHOICE.

I WILL RETURN TO THE TEMPLE AND ENCOURAGE OTHERS TO DO THE SAME. SORA BULQ HAS PROVEN HIMSELF EVIL. THAT WHICH HE SERVES MUST ALSO BE EVIL. EVIL MUST BE OPPOSED.

I WON'T JOIN THE CONFEDERACY, BUT MY OBJECTIONS STILL STAND. THE REPUBLIC IS CORRUPT. I DON'T KNOW HOW WE CAN SERVE IT WITHOUT BEING CORRUPTED OURSELVES.

WHATEVER YOUR CHOICE, WE ON THE COUNCIL WILL *HONOR* IT SO LONG AS IT DOES NOT LEAD YOU TO THE DARK SIDE.

THERE CAN BE NO SCHISM IF WE KEEP OUR HEARTS AND MINDS OPEN TO ONE ANOTHER. WE ARE ALL *ONE* IN THE FORCE.

"WE ARE ALL *JEDI*."

END.

STAR WARS

Anakin Skywalker